IN-LINE SKATES

WHEELS IN MOTION

Morgan Hughes

Rourke

Publishing LLC
Vero Beach, Florida 32964

www.rourkepublishing.com

PHOTO CREDITS: Cover Tom Hauck/Getty Images; title page Spencer Platt/Getty Images; pp 4, 8, 10 Nathan Bilow/Getty Images; p 12 Stanley Chou/Getty Images; p 13 Mike Powell; p 15 Ezra Shaw/Getty Images; pp 17, 18 Mike Simons/Getty Images; p 21 Holly Stein/Getty Images

Title page: *Skating, like biking, is a great way to get around and to get some exercise.*

Editor: Frank Sloan

Cover design by Nicola Stratford

Library of Congress Cataloging-in-Publication Data

Hughes, Morgan, 1957-
 In-line skates / Morgan Hughes.
  v. cm. — (Wheels in motion)
Includes bibliographical references and index.
Contents: In-line skates — Roller skating long ago — The gear — Street — Skate parks — Vert — Extreme skating — Roller skating sports — Safety tips.
 ISBN 1-58952-666-X (hardcover)
 1. In-line skates—Juvenile literature. [1. In-line skating.] I.
Title. II. Series: Hughes, Morgan, 1957- Wheels in motion.
 GV859.73.H84 2003
 796.21—dc21
                                        2003004049

Table of Contents

In-line Skates   5

Roller Skating Long Ago   6

The Gear   9

Street   11

Skate Parks   14

Vert   16

Extreme Skating   19

Roller Skating Sports   20

Safety Tips   22

Glossary   23

Index   24

Further Reading   24

Websites to Visit   24

In-line Skates

The "in-line" skates most popular among today's skaters were invented by a pair of brothers in Minnesota in the 1980s. Scott and Brennan Olson were big hockey fans who didn't want to stop skating in the summer, so they fashioned roller skates that looked like ice skates, with the wheels all in a single line.

Boys and girls of all ages enjoy the speed and freedom of rollerblading.

Roller Skating Long Ago

Compared to the high-tech equipment available today, the first roller skates were very simple. Historians believe a man named Joseph Merlin, from England, invented the first roller skates in the late 1700s. Merlin's skates featured wooden wheels that were attached to the bottom of a pair of leather shoes.

Once upon a time, roller skates clamped on to regular walking shoes.

The Gear

Today's skates are built for comfort, agility, and wear. They have five basic parts: a hard plastic shell for support, a soft liner for comfort, the frame that holds the wheels, and the wheels, which come in various hardness and size. Finally there is a **heel brake**, which allows you to come to a safe stop.

In addition to the skates, important gear includes protective pads.

Street

It doesn't take long for beginners to master the basics of roller skating and start looking for challenges. **Street skaters** get their name because they like to make use of natural outdoor obstacles, such as staircases, curbs, and railings.

Riding the rails is one of the most popular stunts among in-line skaters.

All over the world, in-line skating competitions boast the best of the best.

Showing creative flair is one way in-line skaters earn each other's respect.

Skate Parks

All across the country, skate parks are opening up. These parks are designed especially for roller skaters. They have obstacles—such as **half-pipes** and **ramps**—for advanced skaters and flat lanes for beginners. These parks are great places to master the basics of starting and stopping, crossing over, and skating backward.

Skate parks are shared by in-line skaters and skateboarders alike.

Vert

Vert is short for vertical. It refers to the category of skating that features man-made obstacles like ramps and half-pipes—anything that helps a skater become airborne. This is usually a competitive class of skating for advanced experts.

Strength and agility are necessary to do some of the more advanced tricks.

Extreme Skating

Once you get the hang of roller skating, can stop and start, skate backward smoothly, and do **crossovers** left and right, you'll probably want to push yourself to a higher level. The most difficult skating is extreme skating. It features all the hardest flips, spins, and airborne tricks of the masters.

Intense concentration helps skaters complete even the toughest stunts.

Roller Skating Sports

In addition to in-line skating in specially designed skating parks and on extreme "street" courses, there are many other sports that feature roller skating. Many boys and girls across the country play roller hockey or participate in speed skating, with special skates that resemble speed skates for ice.

Nothing beats a little summer "cement pond" hockey when there's no ice.

Safety Tips

The most important factor in any successful sports activity is safety. In roller skating, even the most accomplished champions wear helmets, **wrist guards**, knee pads, and elbow pads. Everybody falls, but with the correct protective equipment, you can be up and in motion again immediately.

Glossary

crossovers (CROSS oh vurz) — a way to change directions by putting one skate across and in front of the other

half-pipes (HALF PYPZ) — cross-sections of a tube, which look like a length of pipe cut in half horizontally

heel brake (HEAL BRAKE) — a rubber block at the heel of the skate used to slow down and stop

ramps (RAMPZ) — obstacles used for jumps and for gaining speed

street skaters (STREET SKAYTURZ) — expert skaters who find natural obstacles in the street for added challenges

vert (VURT) — short for "vertical," a category of trick skating using manmade obstacles

wrist guards (RIST GAHRDZ) — a combination of hard plastic and a soft pad to protect the wrists in case of a fall

Index

extreme skating   19, 20

frame   9

in-line   5, 20

liner   9

obstacles   11, 14, 16

protective equipment   22

roller hockey   20

safety   22

shell   9

skate parks   14, 20

speed skating   20

street   11

vert   16

Further Reading

Bibbins, Neil. *Bikes, Scooters, Skates, and Boards*. Storey Books
    Publishing, 2002

Crossingham, John. *In-line Skating in Action*. Bt Bound, 2003

Miller, Liz. *Advanced In-line Skating*. Bt Bound, 2000

Shafran, Michael. *Skateboard: Your Guide to Street, Vert, Downhill
    and More*. National Geographic, 2003

Websites To Visit

inlineskating.about.com/mbody.htm

www.iisa.org/

www.skatefaq.com/

www.skating.com/

About The Author

Morgan Hughes is the author of more than 50 books on hockey, track and field, bicycling, and many other subjects. He is also an avid cyclist and professional musician currently living with his family in Connecticut.